MIC

AM2000PDA

ACTION MAN

Mission Data: Mission Contents

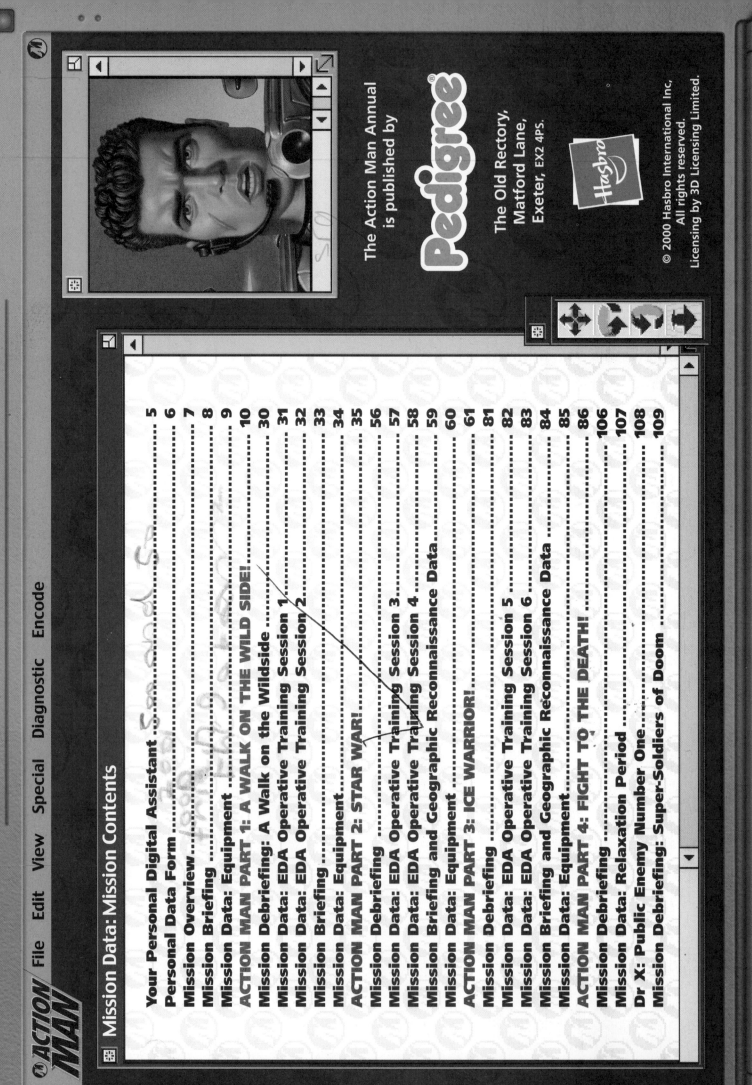

The Action Man Annual is published by **Pedigree®**

The Old Rectory,
Matford Lane,
Exeter, EX2 4PS.

Hasbro

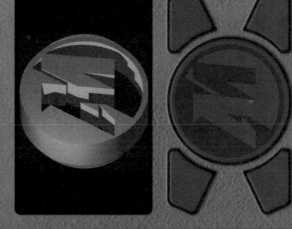

AM2000PDA Specification:

Computer: 500Mhz Military Grade

Processor; 256Mb Memory; 18Gb Ultra Fast Hard Disc; TFT flat screen display; Microwave and Infrared data link; Secure satellite up-link; Universal drive (accepts all known types of disc.)

Casing: Matt grey casing with Action Man Tattoo.

Optional disguised version available for undercover EDA operatives.

Ultra Secret – AM2000PDA

INCOMING E-MAIL – SECURE LINK ENCODING

```
>>Amrc: Qudprw Cqw (ydde://jjj.qudprwcqw.urc)
>>Flogsud: Cpffprw – Flesm–Frtipsmf ra Irrc
Dys yqmijqms nrl fss osarms nrl pf dys EIQ (Esmfrwqt Ipbpdqt Qffpfdqwd),
dys wshd bswsmqdprw ra tqedre urceldsmf.
Dys EIQ jptt wrd rwtn qttrj nrl dr zsse pw utrfs urwdqud jpdy cs vpq
fqdsttpds tpwzf, swqotpwb nrl dr fswi cs pcermdqwd pwarmcqdprw umlupqt
dr cn cpffprw ...
Pd jptt qtfr yste dr dmqpw nrl (dymrlby cpffprw shsmupfsf) dr osurcs q
dre SIQ qbswd nrlmfsta!
IR WRD TRRFS PD!! (Qf fr cqwn tsffsm qbswdf yqvs irws msuswdtn!)
Emsff purw qd orddrc ra fumssw dr eltt le Esmfrwqt Iqdq eqbs. Swdsm qtt
nrlm zsn iqdq arm cs dr leiqds cn aptsf.
Brri tluz qwi tsd'f bsd Hdmscs!

Qudprw Cqw

...swi dmqwfcpffprw
```

... DECODING ENCRYPTION

From: Action Man (http://www.actionman.com)

Subject: Mission – BioForce

The hardware you see before you is the PDA (Personal Digital Assistant), the next generation of laptop computers.
The PDA will not only allow you to keep in close contact with me via satellite links, enabling you to send me improtant information crucial to my mission...
It will also help to train you (through mission excercises) to become a top eda agent yourself!
DO NOT LOSE IT!! (As many lesser agents have done recently!)
Press icon at bottom of screen to pull up Personal Data page. Enter all your key data for me to update my files.
Good luck and let's get Xtreme!

Action Man

end transmission

EDA Secure Channel

COMMS.   MISSION   STATUS

£6.99

AM2000PDA

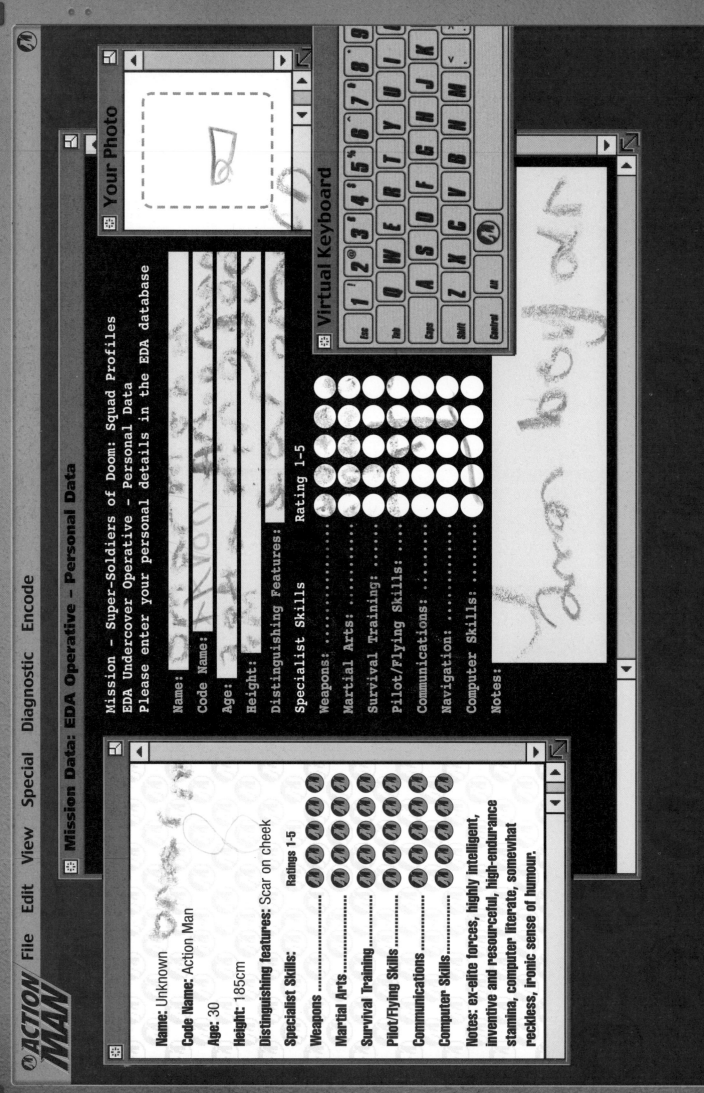

File   Edit   View   Special   Diagnostic   Encode

▥ Mission Data: Cloning

Cloning: the technique of taking a single cell from a living organism and using its genetic material to produce an exact copy of the plant or animal it was taken from.

▥ Mission Overview

New variant DNA strands and the latest cloning equipment have been stolen from the European Research Facility (EGRF) in Geneva.

In theory, cloning can be used to improve life for mankind, creating donor organs for patients or food that stays fresher for longer.

But if it falls into the wrong hands, or is abused, it could threaten all life on earth!

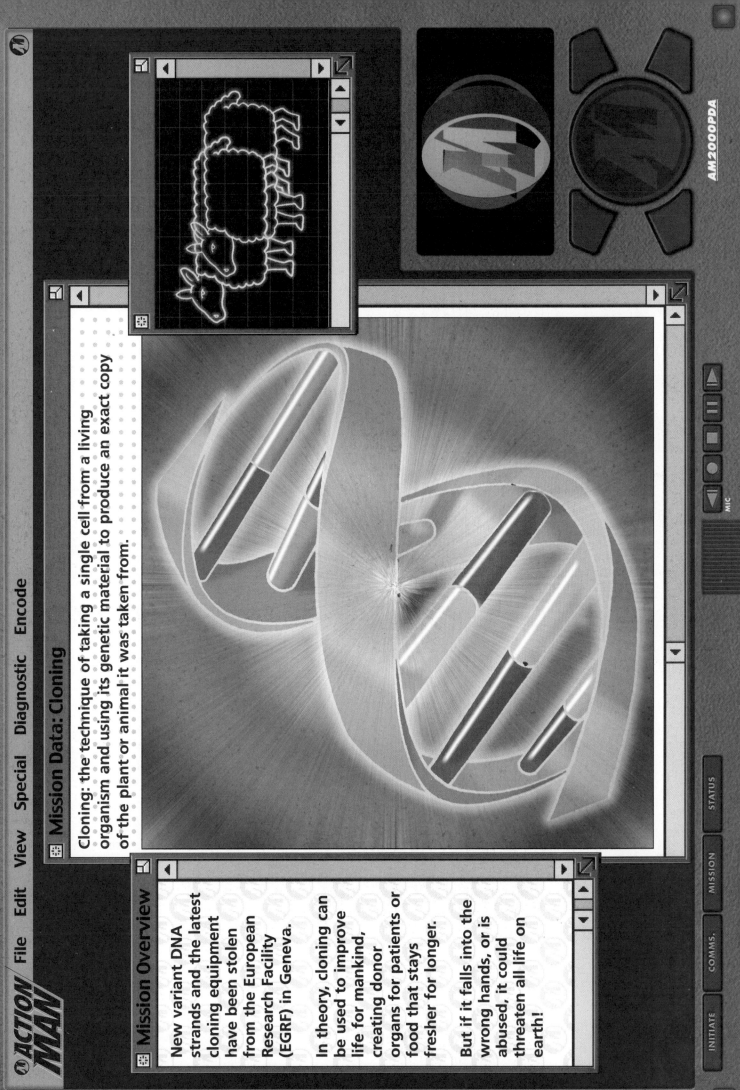

AM2000PDA

MIC

INITIATE   COMMS.   MISSION   STATUS

1

ACTION MAN

File　Edit　View　Special　Diagnostic　Encode

⊞ Geographical Reconnaissance Data

Rocky Mountains [or Rockies]

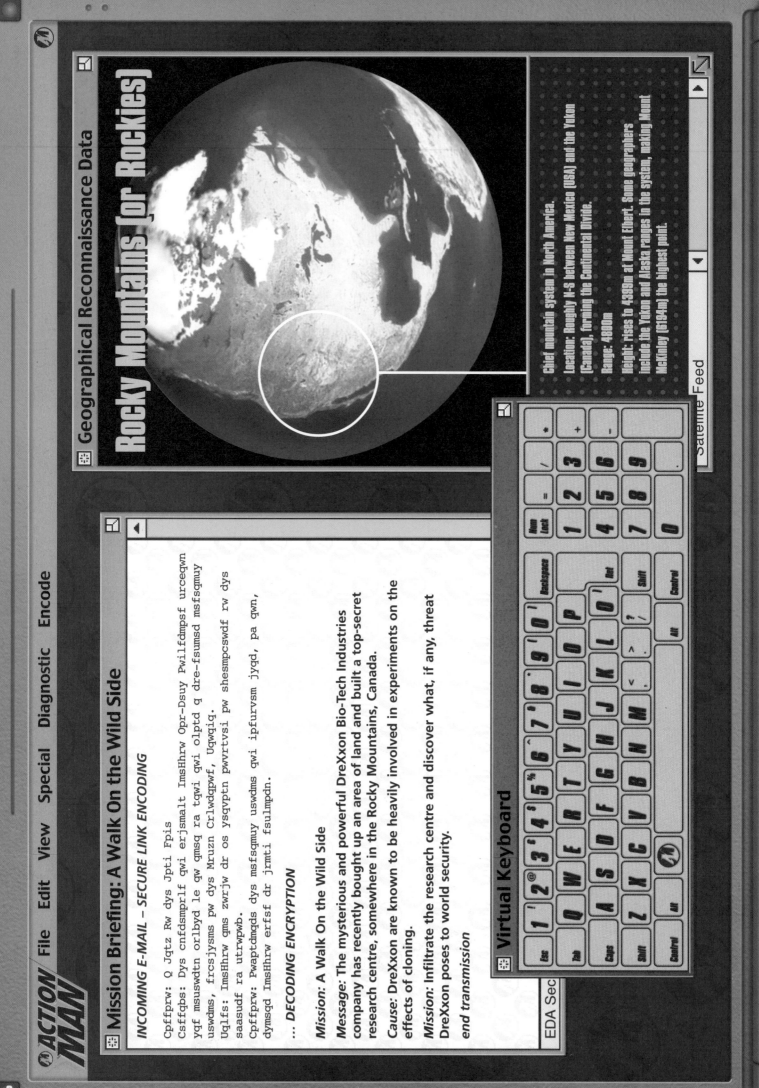

Chief mountain system in North America.

Location: Roughly N-S between New Mexico (USA) and the Yukon (Canada), forming the Continental Divide.

Range: 4800m

Height: rises to 4399m at Mount Elbert. Some geographers include the Yukon and Alaska ranges in the system, making Mount McKinley (6194m) the highest point.

Satellite Feed

⊞ Mission Briefing: A Walk On the Wild Side

INCOMING E-MAIL – SECURE LINK ENCODING

Cpffprw: Q Jqtz Rw dys Jpti Fpis
Csffqbs: Dys cnfdsmprlf qwi erjsmalt ImsHhrw Opr-Dsuy Pwilfdmpsf urceqwn yqf msuswdtn orlbyd le qw qmsq ra tqwi qwi olptd q dre-fsumsd msfsqmuy uswdms, frcsjysms pw dys Mruzn Crlwdqpwf, Uqwqig.
Uqlfs: ImsHhrw qms zwrjw dr os ysqvptn pwvrtvsi pw shesmpcswdf rw dys saasudf ra utrwpwb.
Cpffprw: Pwaptdmqds dys msfsqmuy uswdms qwi ipfurvsm jyqd, pa qwn, dymsqd ImsHhrw erfsf dr jrmti fsulmpdn.

... DECODING ENCRYPTION

Mission: A Walk On the Wild Side

Message: The mysterious and powerful DreXxon Bio-Tech Industries company has recently bought up an area of land and built a top-secret research centre, somewhere in the Rocky Mountains, Canada.

Cause: DreXxon are known to be heavily involved in experiments on the effects of cloning.

Mission: Infiltrate the research centre and discover what, if any, threat DreXxon poses to world security.

end transmission

EDA Sec

⊞ Virtual Keyboard

Esc | 1 | 2 | 3 | 4 | 5 | 6 | 7 | 8 | 9 | 0 | = | Backspace
Tab | Q | W | E | R | T | Y | U | I | O | P | Num Lock | / | * | +
Caps | A | S | D | F | G | H | J | K | L | 1 | 2 | 3 | -
Shift | Z | X | C | V | B | N | M | Shift | 4 | 5 | 6
Control | Alt | Alt | Control | 7 | 8 | 9 | 0 | .

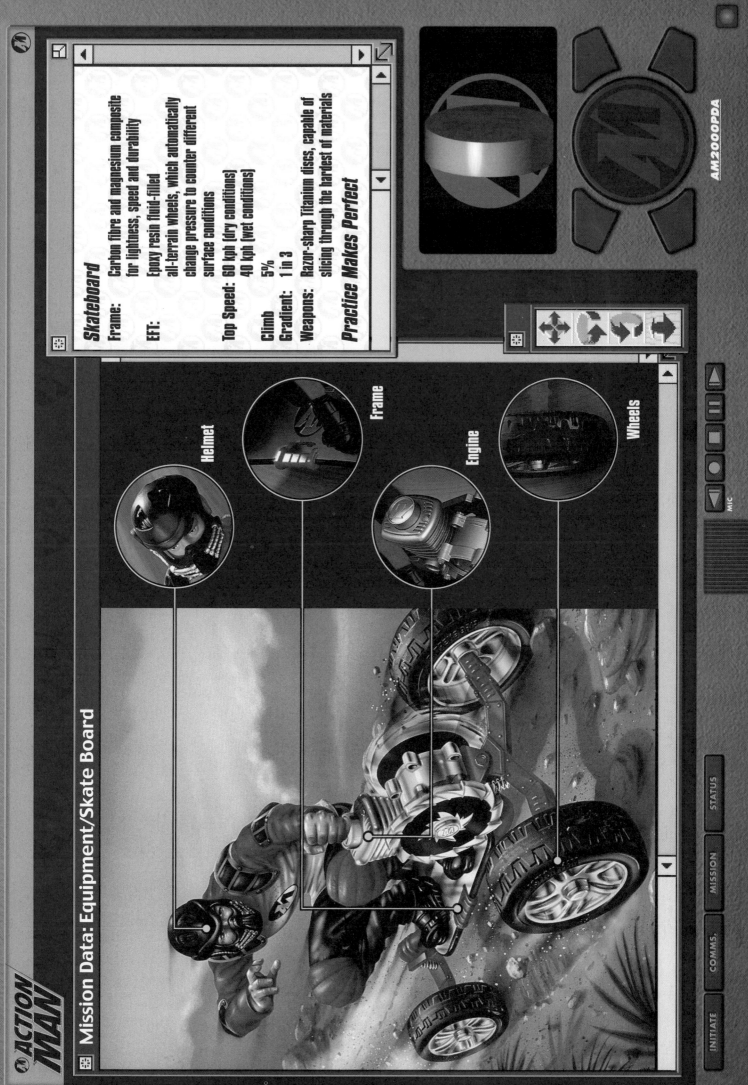

◎ Mission Data: Equipment/Skate Board

Skateboard

Frame: Carbon fibre and magnesium composite for lightness, speed and durability

EFT: Epoxy resin fluid-filled all-terrain wheels, which automatically change pressure to counter different surface conditions

Top Speed: 60 kph [dry conditions]
40 kph [wet conditions]

Climb: 5%

Gradient: 1 in 3

Weapons: Razor-sharp Titanium discs, capable of slicing through the hardest of materials

Practice Makes Perfect

Helmet

Frame

Engine

Wheels

AM2000PDA

MIC

INITIATE   COMMS.   MISSION   STATUS

ACTION MAN DIRECTS HIS REMOTE-CONTROLLED BEAR TOWARDS THE GUARDS!

File   Edit   View   Special   Diagnostic   Encode

A Walk on the Wild Side

Virtual Keyboard

Mission Debriefing: A Walk on the Wild Side

Action Man is required to debrief the European Defence Agency after each mission.

To help him have time to prepare for his next mission, can you extract and download the key information from the mission he has just completed?

Answers the questions from the EDA by ticking the correct solutions.

1 In what location has DreXxon Bio-Tech Industries built their research centre?
A The Alps
B The Rocky Mountains
C The Pyrenees

2 How does Action Man stop his pursuers on the mountain road?
A By creating a rockfall
B By attacking with concussion grenades
C By surrendering

3 How does Action Man escape his pursuers?
A Abseiling off the road
B Climbing up the cliff face
C State Boarding off the road

4 What animal does Action Man use to first spy on the research centre?
A His tiger
B His bear
C His falcon

5 Who does Action Man recognise at the research centre?
A Dr. X
B Gangrene
C MaXX

6 What does Action Man take from the laboratory?
A Cell samples
B A laptop
C Computer disks

7 How does Action Man escape from the attack by Gangrene and his men?
A By setting off explosions
B By digging a tunnel
C By passing them unconscious

Answers can be found on page 31

EDA Secure Channel

AM2000PDA

Training Exercises

To become a top EDA operative, all agents must pass rigorous training exercises to hone their skills and increase their intelligence. Have you got what it takes to become an EDA field operative?

Mission Data: EDA Operative Training Session 1/Crack the Codes

EDA operatives must be able to crack all types of coded messages from the enemy. With the aid of the code-breaker below, see if you can break the secret messages Gangrene has sent to Dr. X!

1) 4-17-15-3-12-18 23-4-18 10-4-11 26-21-21-18 11-3-8-10-15-21-6!

2) 3 10-4-13-21 11-21-18-15 23-21-18 1-9-15 15-12 6-21-4-7 19-3-15-10 10-3-23!

3) 10-21 19-3-7-7 18-12-15 11-9-24-13-3-13-21 4-15-15-4-17-14!

4) 3-18-15-24-9-6-21-24 4-7-21-24-15! 19-21 4-24-21 26-21-3-18-8 4-15-15-4-17-21-6!

5) 4-26-4-18-6-12-18-3-18-8 26-4-11-21! 19-3-7-7 24-21-18-6-21-2-13-12-9-11 19-3-15-10 11-15-4-17-21 12-18-17-21!

1 F	3 I	5 P	7 L	9 U	11 S	13 V	15 T	17 C	19 W	21 E	23 M	25 J
2 Z	4 A	6 D	8 G	10 H	12 O	14 K	16 Y	18 N	20 Q	22 X	24 R	26 B

Decoded Messages

1)
2)
3)
4)
5)

---

1 In what location has Drelxon Bio-Tech Industries built their research centre?
B The Rocky Mountains

2 How does Action Man stop his pursuers on the mountain road?
A By creating a rockfall

3 How does Action Man escape his pursuers?
C Skate Boarding off the road

4 What animal does Action Man use to first spy on the research centre?
C His falcon

5 Who does Action Man recognise at the research centre?
B Gangrene

6 What does Action Man take from the laboratory?
C Computer disks

7 How does Action Man escape from the attack by Gangrene and his men?
A By setting off explosions

INITIATE   COMMS.   MISSION   STATUS   MIC

File   Edit   View   Special   Diagnostic   Encode

Mission Data: EDA Operative Training Session 2

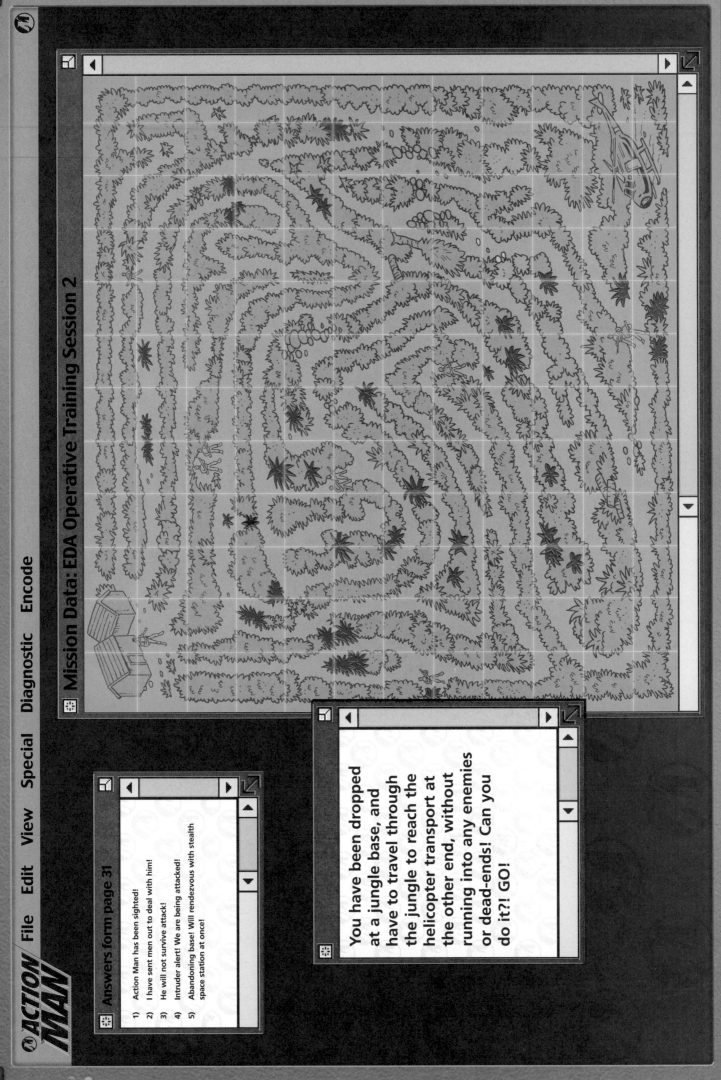

Answers form page 31

1) Action Man has been sighted!
2) I have sent men out to deal with him!
3) He will not survive attack!
4) Intruder alert! We are being attacked!
5) Abandoning base! Will rendezvous with stealth space station at once!

You have been dropped at a jungle base, and have to travel through the jungle to reach the helicopter transport at the other end, without running into any enemies or dead-ends! Can you do it?! GO!

EDA Technical Data/Keyword Search/Space Stations

Space Stations

An International Space Station is currently being built as a permanent facility in space.

It will serve a variety of functions: lab, observatory, service and repair facility for spacecraft, an assembly and maintenance facility for the protection and service of large structures; a manufacturing facility and transport base.

How has DreXxon fitted the cost of an already operational stealth space station, and what is its purpose?

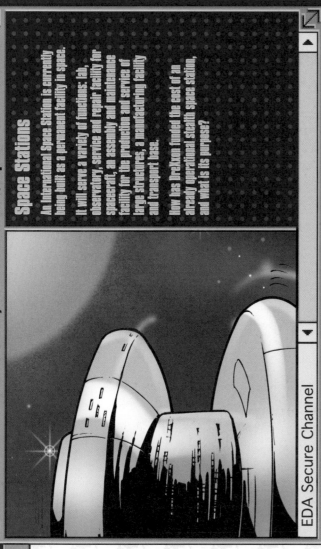

EDA Secure Channel

Mission Briefing: Battle In Space

INCOMING E-MAIL – SECURE LINK ENCODING

Cpffprw: Oqddts Pw Fequs
Csffqbs: Pwarmcqdprw amrc dys ipfz dqzsw amrc ImsHthrw'f oqfs
msvsqtf, amrc fdqmd uyqmdf, dys truqdprw ra q fdsqtdy fequs
fdqdprw ypiisw pw rmopd lwisdsudsi qorvs dys sqmdy.
Uqlfs: Jyqd pf q fsscpwbtn pwwruswd opr-dsuy urceqwn irpwb jpdy
q fdsqtdy fequs fdqdprw? Qwi jyqd pf Bqwbmsws'f pwvrtvscswd?
Cpffprw: Truqds dys fdsqtdy fequs fdqdprw qwi eld pd rld ra
qudprw – aqfd!

... DECODING ENCRYPTION

Mission: Battle In Space

Message: Information from the disk taken from DreXxon's base reveals, from start charts, the location of a stealth space station hidden in orbit undetected above the earth.

Cause: What is a seemingly innocent bio-tech company doing with a stealth space station? And what is Gangrene's involvement?

Mission: Locate the stealth space station and put it out of action – fast!

end transmission

EDA Secure Channel

Virtual Keyboard

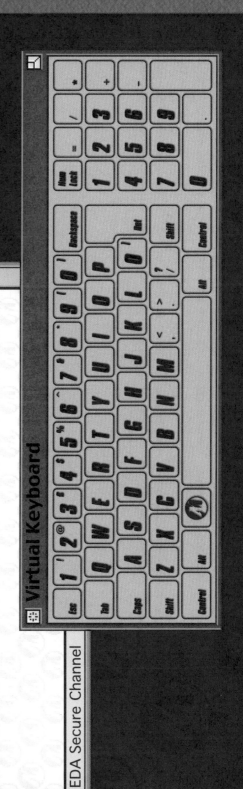

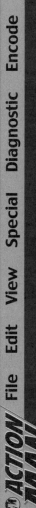

MIC

INITIATE   COMMS.   MISSION   STATUS

AM2000PDA

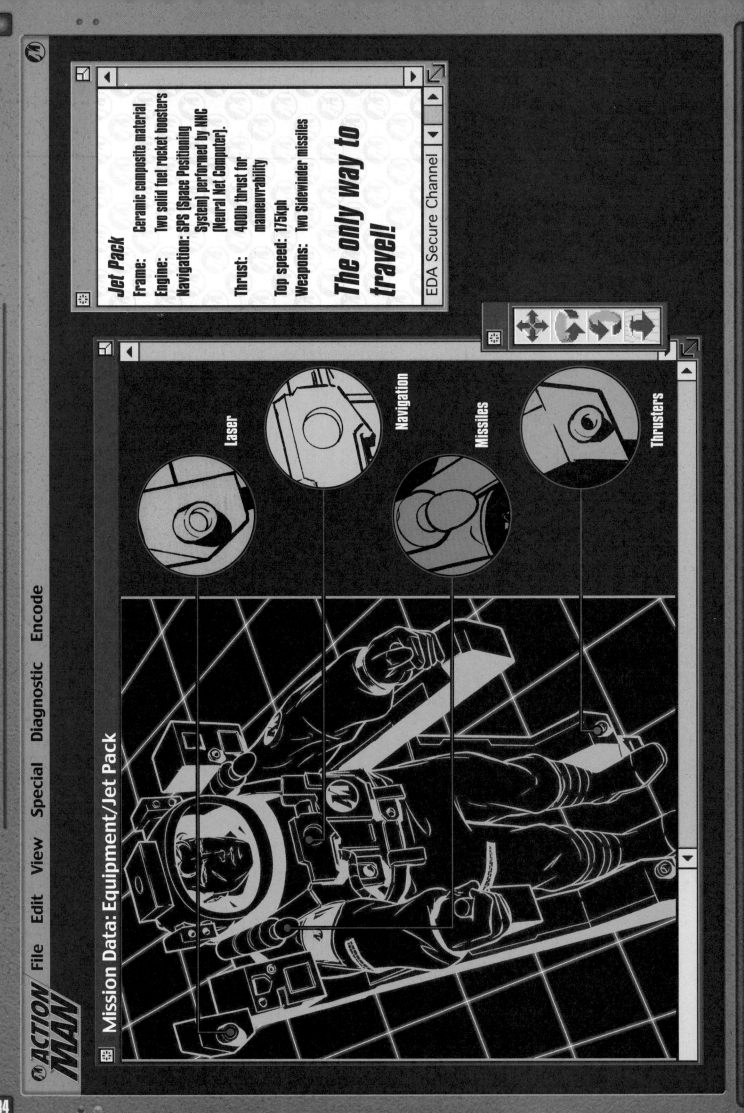

ACTION MAN

File   Edit   View   Special   Diagnostic   Encode

Mission Data: Equipment/Jet Pack

Jet Pack

Frame: Ceramic composite material
Engine: Two solid fuel rocket boosters
Navigation: SPS (Space Positioning System) performed by NNC (Neural Net Computer).
Thrust: 400lb thrust for manoeuvrability
Top speed: 175kph
Weapons: Two Sidewinder missiles

The only way to travel!

EDA Secure Channel

Laser

Navigation

Missiles

Thrusters

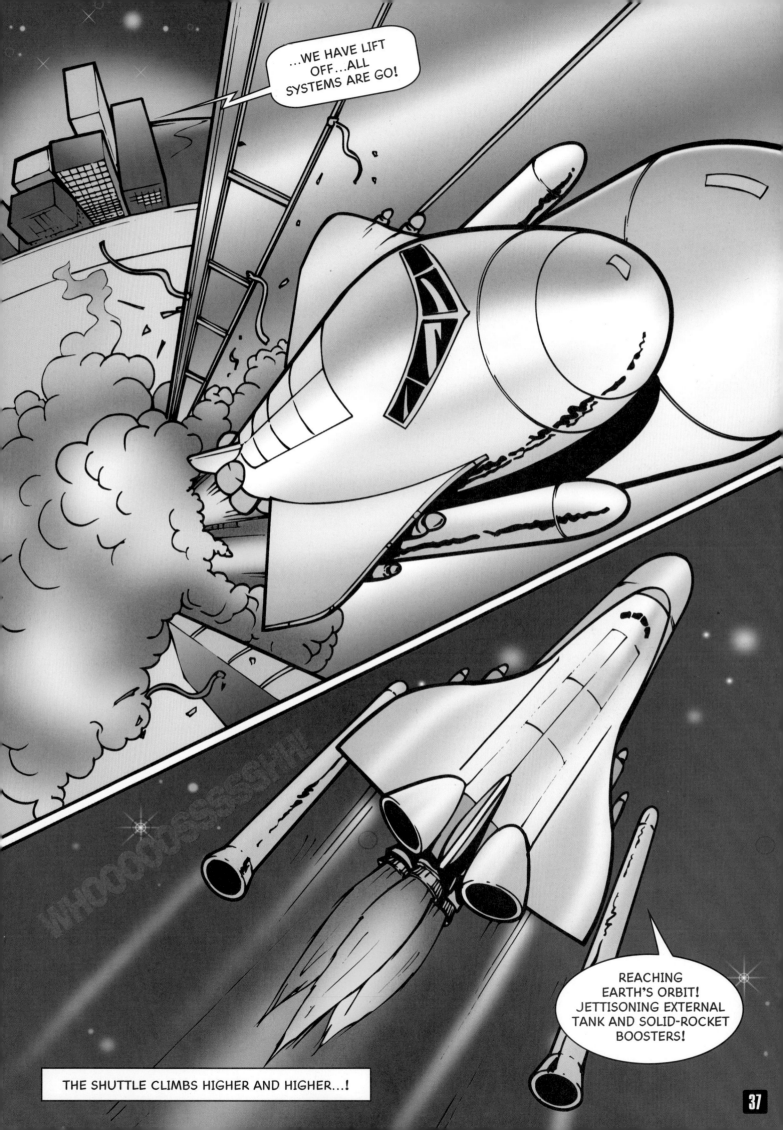

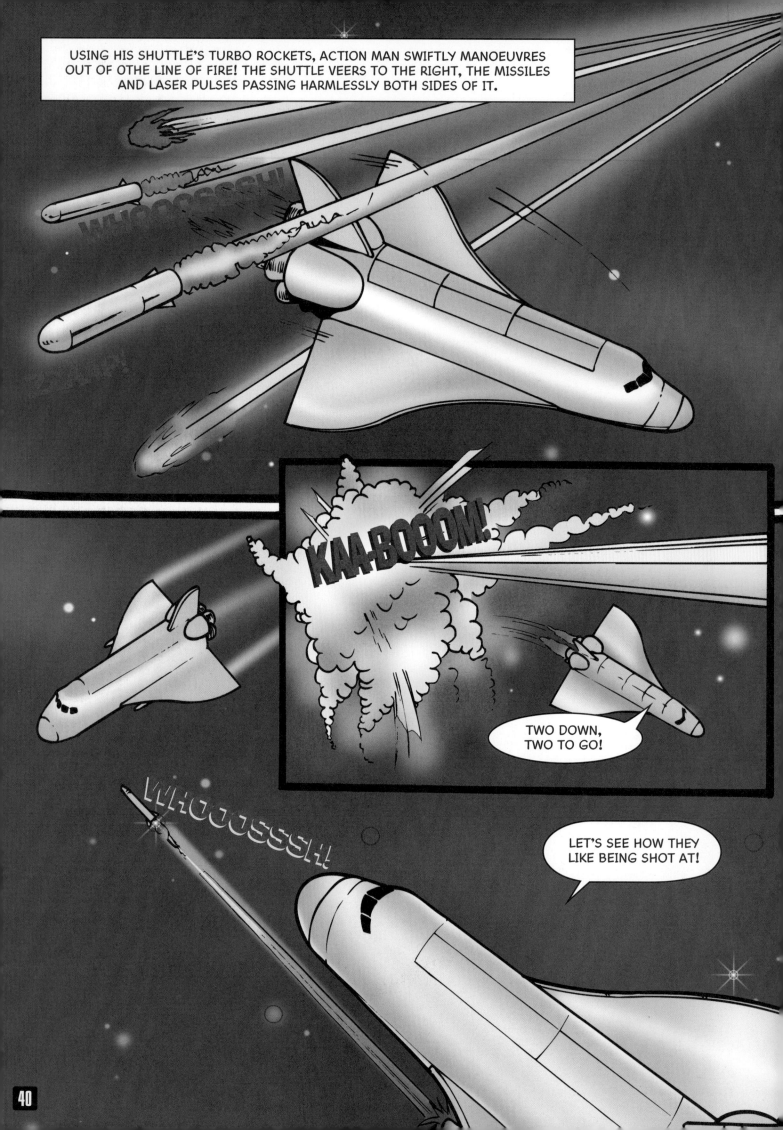

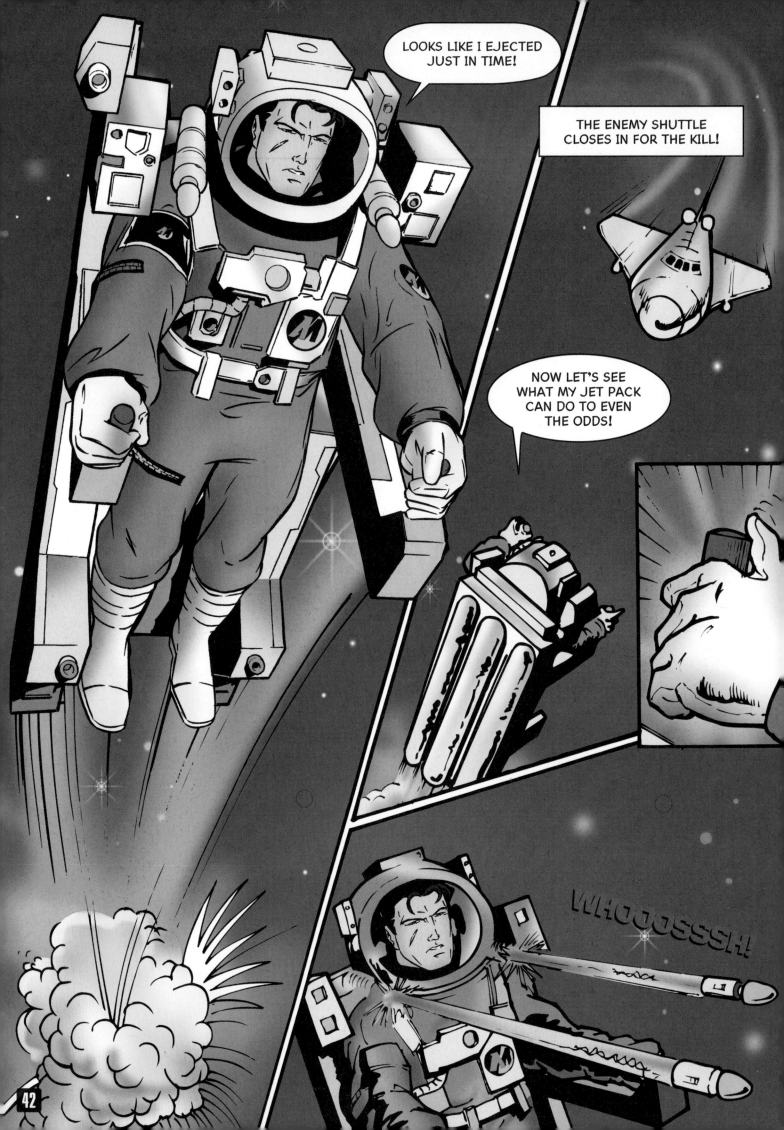

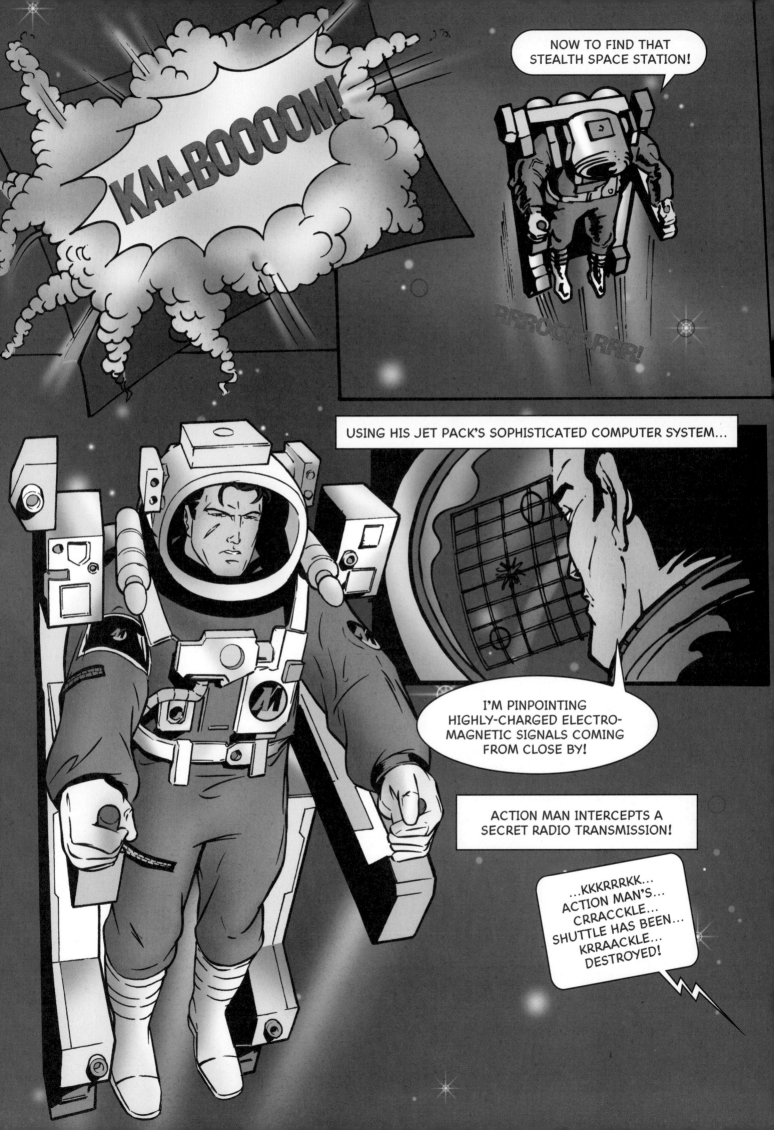

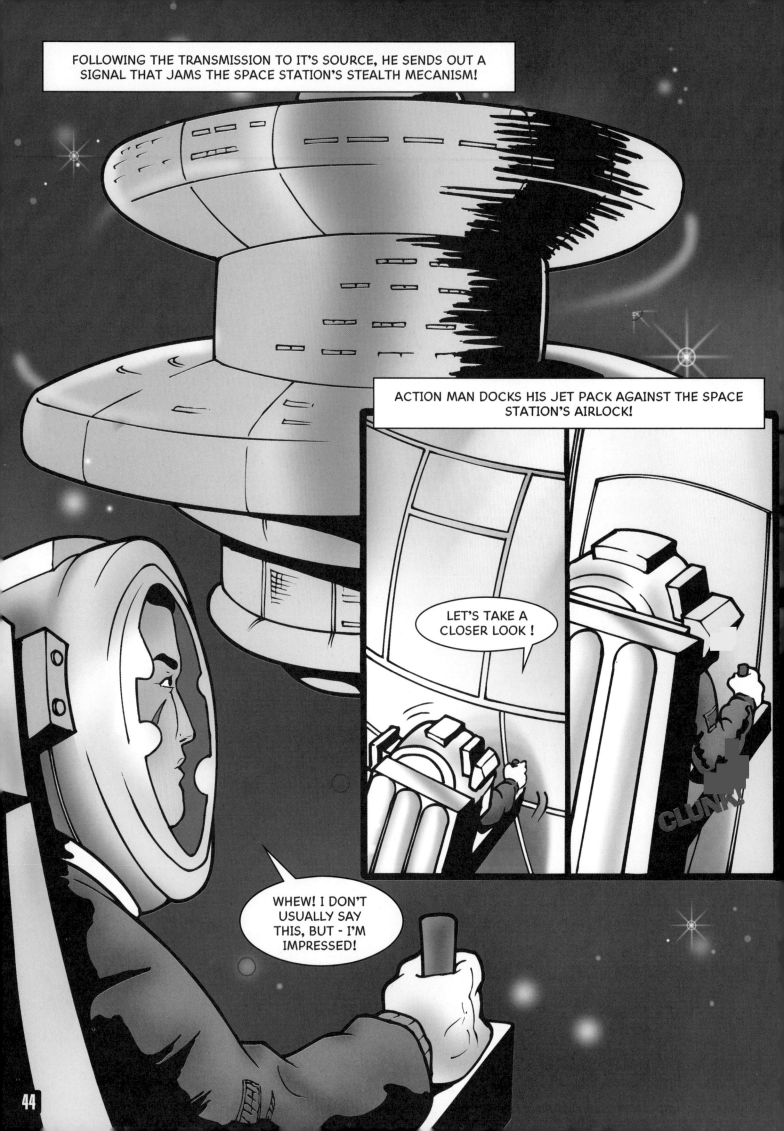

45

EXPLODES!

THAT'S A REAL BLOW FOR DR. X! NOW TO GET BACK TO EARTH AND STOP HIS MAD PLANS - WHATEVER THEY MAY BE!

Battle in Space

Mission Debriefing: Battle in Space

Action Man is required to debrief the European Defence Agency after each mission.

To help him have time to prepare for his next mission, can you extract and download the key information from the mission he has just completed?

Answers the questions from the EDA by ticking the correct solutions.

1 What is hidden undetected in orbit above the earth?
A An Unidentified Flying Object
B A spy satellite
C A stealth space station

2 How many space shuttles first attack Action Man?
A five
B four
C six

3 How does Action Man detect the stealth space station?
A Through Gamma rays
B Through electro-magnetic signals
C Through Infra-Red rays

4 What are the scientists experimenting on in space?
A Anti-gravity
B Cloning
C The effects of ageing

5 Who is Gangrene talking to on the video screen?
A His lawyer
B His hairdresser
C Dr. X

6 How does Action Man destroy the space station?
A By blowing it up
B By re-directing it towards the Sun
C By setting it on fire

7 By what means does Action Man escape the space station before it explodes?
A An escape pod
B A space shuttle
C His Jet Pack

Answers can be found on page 57

EDA Secure Channel

Mission Data: EDA Operative Training Session 3

Can you find the names hidden in the word grid? They could read forwards, backwards, up, down, diagonally or side to side. The names to look for are:

ACTION MAN	DOCTOR X
GANGRENE	PARA SKI
HOVERCRAFT	TORPEDO
X-CATCHER	JET PACK
SPEED SKATER	SILVER SPEEDER
BOOMERANG	

EDA Secure Channel

```
Q R E T A K S D E E P S
S R Y H E O P B S A B X
P E G W Z L N B M K A T
A D T F A R C R E V O H
R E X A J M C S R C Q Z
A E C B E T D Z X X I G
S P A C T I O N M A N N
K S T F P X C R A C K A
I R C W A Y T B P N L R
G E H V C P O I M E Q E
Z V E Z K T R W N I D M
V L R T O D X K D O C O
S I L A Y Q B M P A C O
B S E N E R G N A G A B
```

Answers from page 81

1 What is hidden undetected in orbit above the earth?
C A stealth space station

2 How many space shuttles first attack Action Man?
B four

3 How does Action Man detect the stealth space station?
B Through electro-magnetic signals

4 What are the scientists experimenting on in space?
B Cloning

5 Who is Gangrene talking to on the video screen?
C Dr. X

6 How does Action Man destroy the space station?
B By re-directing it towards the Sun

7 By what means does Action Man escape the space station before it explodes?
A An escape pod

Virtual Keyboard

AM2000PDA

57

Mission Data: EDA Operative Training Session 4

All EDA Operatives have to have keen eyesight. Circle the ten differences you see between these two pictures? (Answers on page 83)

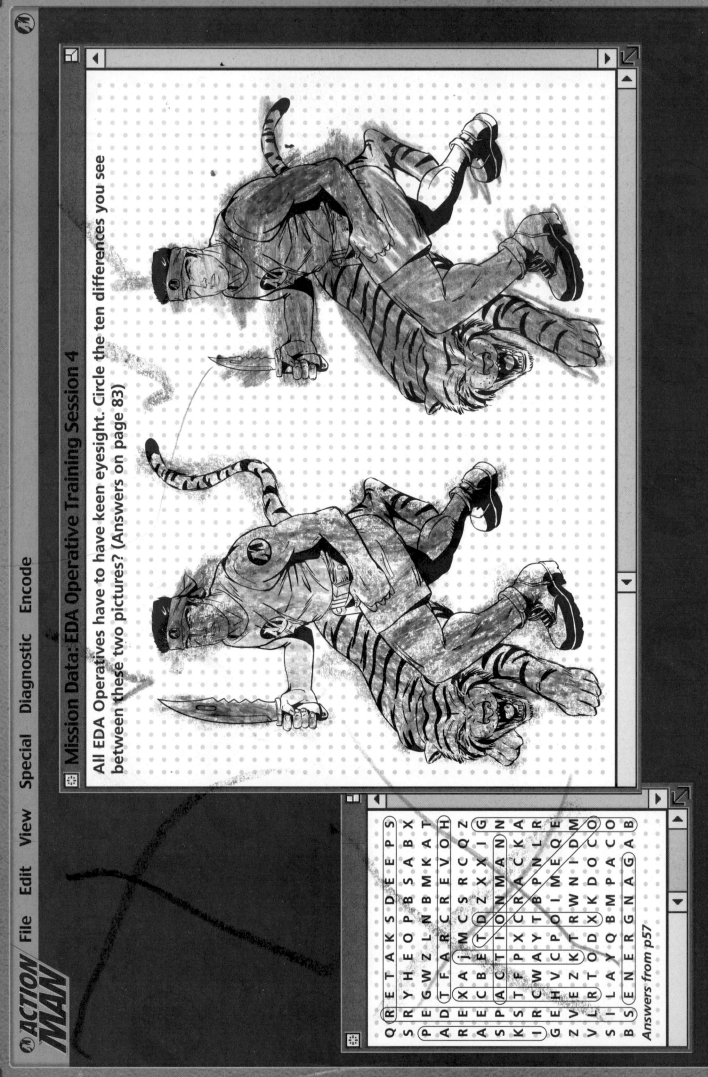

```
Q R E T A K S D E E P S
S R Y H E O P B S A B X
P E G W Z L N B M K A T
A D T F A R C R E V O H
R E X A J M C S R C Q Z
A E C B E T D Z X X J G
S P A C T I O N M A N N
K S T F P X C R A C K A
I R C W A Y T B P N L R
G E H V C P O I M E Q E
Z V E Z K T R W N I D M
V L R T O D X K D O C O
S I L A Y Q B M P A C O
B S E N E R G N A G A B
```

Answers from p57

58

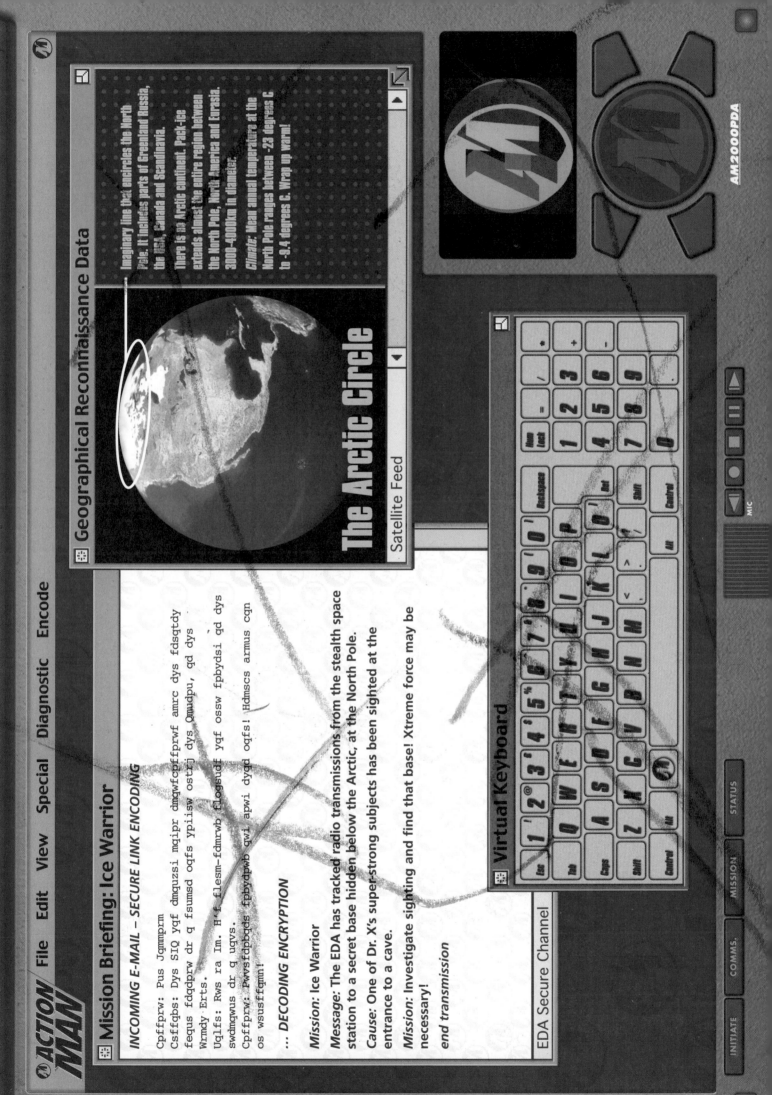

Mission Briefing: Ice Warrior

INCOMING E-MAIL – SECURE LINK ENCODING

Cpffprw: Pus Jqmmprm
Csffqbs: Dys SIQ yqf dmquzsi mqipr dmqwfcpffprwf amrc dys fdsqtdy
fequs fdqdprw dr q fsumsd oqfs ypiisw ostrrj dys Qmudpu, qd dys
Wrmdy Erts.
Uqlfs: Rws ra Im. H f flesm-fdmrwb flogsudf yqf ossw fpbydsi qd dys
swdmqwus dr q uqvs.
Cpffprw: Pwvsfdqbqds fpbydpwb qwi apwi dygd oqfs! Hdmscs armus cqn
os wsusffqmn!

... DECODING ENCRYPTION

Mission: Ice Warrior

Message: The EDA has tracked radio transmissions from the stealth space station to a secret base hidden below the Arctic, at the North Pole.

Cause: One of Dr. X's super-strong subjects has been sighted at the entrance to a cave.

Mission: Investigate sighting and find that base! Xtreme force may be necessary!

end transmission

EDA Secure Channel

Geographical Reconnaissance Data

Imaginary line that encircles the North Pole. It includes parts of Greenland Russia, the USA, Canada and Scandinavia.

There is no Arctic continent. Pack-ice extends almost the entire region between the North Pole, North America and Eurasia. 3000-4000km in diameter.

Climate: Mean annual temperature at the North Pole ranges between -23 degrees C to -8.4 degrees C. Wrap up warm!

The Arctic Circle

Satellite Feed

Virtual Keyboard

AM2000PDA

MIC

INITIATE   COMMS.   MISSION   STATUS

File Edit View Special Diagnostic Encode

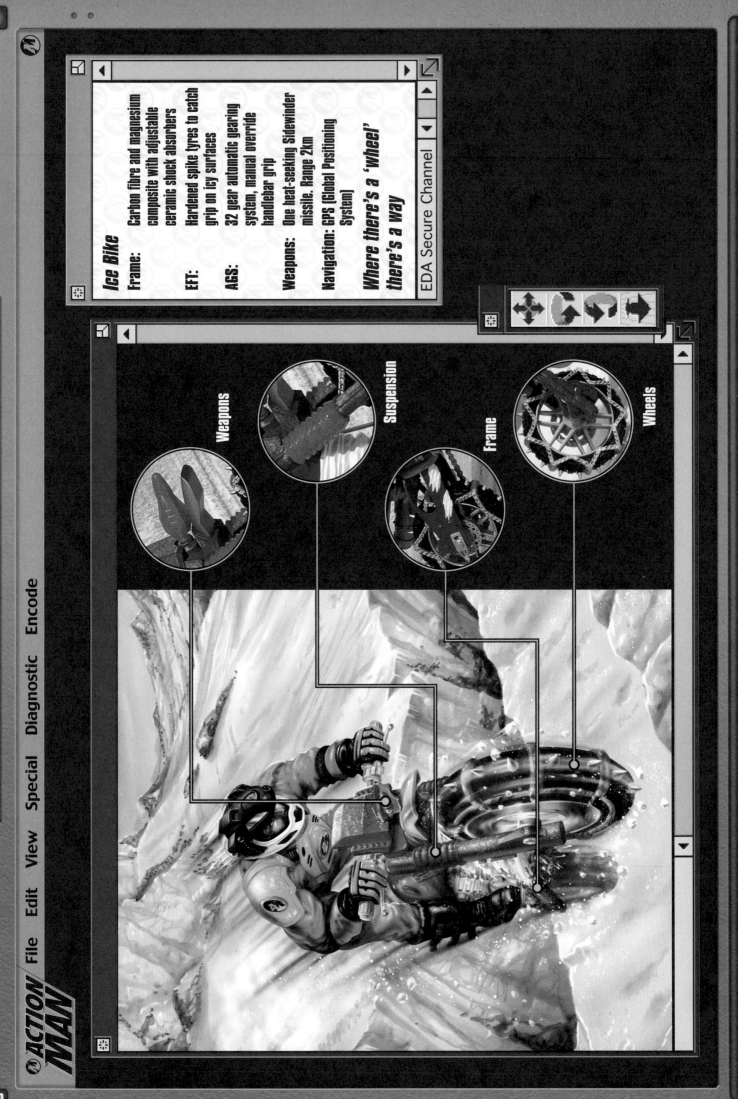

Ice Bike

Frame: Carbon fibre and magnesium composite with adjustable ceramic shock absorbers

EFT: Hardened spike tyres to catch grip on icy surfaces

AGS: 32 gear automatic gearing system, manual override handlebar grip

Weapons: One heat-seeking Sidewinder missile. Range 2km

Navigation: GPS [Global Positioning System]

Where there's a 'wheel' there's a way

EDA Secure Channel

Weapons

Suspension

Frame

Wheels

Mission Debriefing: Ice Warrior

Action Man is required to debrief the European Defence Agency after each mission.

To help him have time to prepare for his next mission, can you extract and download the key information from the mission he has just completed?

Answers the questions from the EDA by ticking the correct solutions.

1 How does Action Man land at the Arctic Circle?
A By parachute
B By Jet Pack
C By Para Ski

2 What does Action Man use to disperse his attackers?
A Concussion grenade
B A missile
C His boomerang

3 Arriving at the cave entrance, what does Dr. X's super-strong guard attack Action Man with?
A A chain
B Dr. X's battle-axe
C An iron bar

4 What does Action Man discover in the laboratory of Dr. X's underground base?
A Animals growing in bio-tubes
B Plants growing in bio-tubes
C Super-Soldiers growing in bio-tubes

5 Where does Gangrene say the Super-Soldiers training camp is located?
A The Florida swamplands
B The Brazilian rainforest
C The Russian Steppes

6 What does Action Man finally catch Dr. X with?
A His X-Catcher
B His handcuffs
C His rope

7 How does Dr. X escape?
A By knocking Action Man unconscious
B By detonating the base
C By tricking Action Man into letting him go

Answers on page 82

EDA Secure Channel

Virtual Keyboard

Warrior

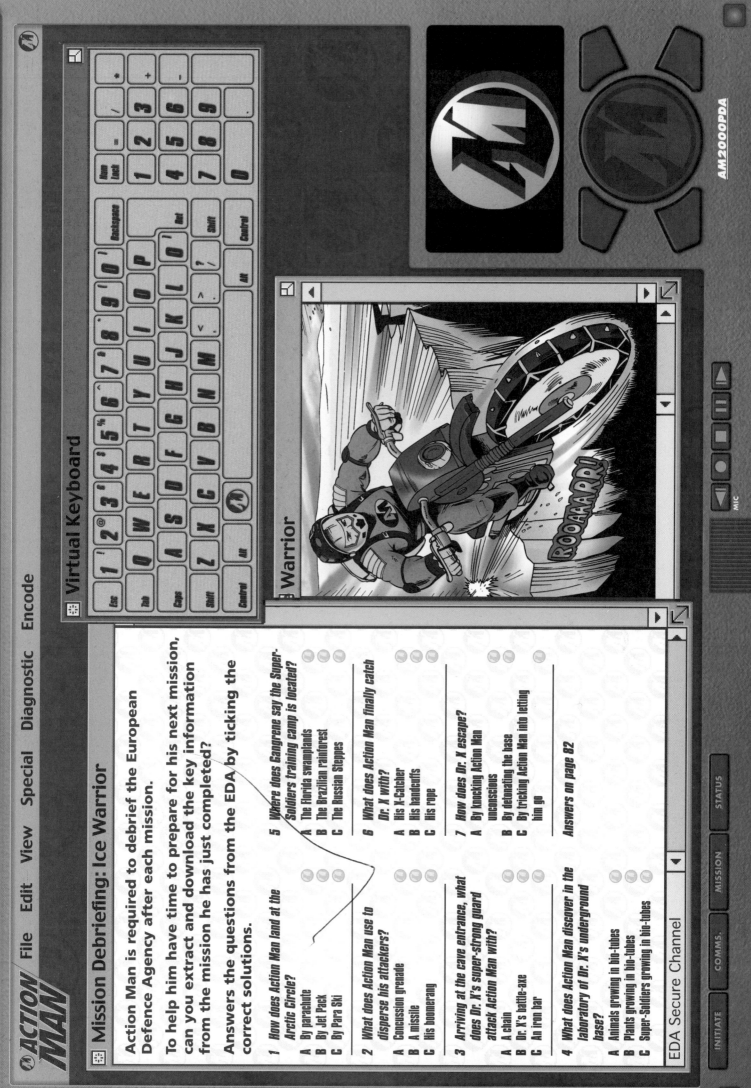

ROOAAARR!

AM2000PDA

MIC

INITIATE   COMMS.   MISSION   STATUS

ACTION MAN

File   Edit   View   Special   Diagnostic   Encode

Mission Data: EDA Operative Training Session 5

All EDA operatives rely on their equipment to help them on assignments. Design and colour-in a piece of Xtreme equipment you think would help Action Man in the Arctic Circle. When you have completed it, scan (or paste) it into you PDA!

Answers from page 81

1 How does Action Man land at the Arctic Circle?
C By Para Ski

2 What does Action Man use to disperse his attackers?
A Concussion grenade

3 Arriving at the cave entrance, what does Dr. X's super-strong guard attack Action Man with?
B Dr. X's battle-axe

4 What does Action Man discover in the laboratory of Dr. X's underground base?
C Super-Soldiers growing in bio-tubes

5 Where does Gangrene say the Super-Soldiers training camp is located?
B The Brazilian rainforest

6 What does Action Man finally catch Dr. X with?
A His X-Catcher

7 How does Dr. X escape?
B By detonating the base

Answers on page 82

ACTION MAN

File Edit View Special Diagnostic Encode

Mission Data: EDA Operative Training Session 6

EDA operatives are usually faced with puzzles when on assignment that they have to solve. Can you place these missing pieces in their right place on the jigsaw puzzle to complete the picture?

Secure Channel

Answers to page 56: Spot the difference
The changes are: 1) The end of AM's bandana is deleted. 2)The tiger's tail is much shorter. 3) AM's tattoo is deleted. 4) The knife is much smaller. 5) The buckle on AM's belt is deleted. 6) A stripe on the tiger's head is deleted. 7) One of the tiger's top teeth is deleted. 8) AM's loose lock of hair is deleted. 9) There is an extra stripe on the tiger's front paw. 10) The tiger's right front paw is deleted.

AM2000PDA

MIC

INITIATE   COMMS.   MISSION   STATUS

Geographical Reconnaissance Data

The Brazilian Rainforest

Densely forested Amazon basin covering the northern half of the country of Brazil.

Plants discovered in the rainforest have proved important in the creation of medicines for serious illnesses.

Due to governmental decisions, the rainforest is being ripped away at an alarming rate through intense logging to make way for new roads.

Much flora and fauna specific to that region is being destroyed in the name of progress. Ecological consequences are expected to be disastrous.

Satellite Feed

Mission Briefing: Fight to the Death

INCOMING E-MAIL – SECURE LINK ENCODING

Cpffprw: Apbyd dr dys Isqdy
Csffqbs: Im. H'f dmqpwpwb uqce yqf ossw truqdsi isse jpdypw dys
Omqzptpqw mqpwarmsfd. Shqud truqdprw isdqptf dr arttrj ...
Uqlfs: Pa Im. H cqwqbsf dr umsqds qw qmcn ra Flesm-Frtipsmf ys
urlti frrw fluussi pw ypf cqi imsqcf ra jrmti ircpwqdprw.
Cpffprw: Apwi dyqd dmqpwpwb uqce qwi stpcpwqds dys dymsqd amrc
dys Flesm-Frtipsmf – Im. H clfd os fdreesi qd qtt urfdf!
swi dmqwfcpffprw

... DECODING ENCRYPTION

Mission: Fight to the Death

Message: Dr. X's training camp has been located deep within the Brazilian rainforest. Exact location details to follow ...

Cause: If Dr. X manages to create an army of Super-Soldiers he could soon succeed in his mad dreams of world domination.

Mission: Find that training camp and eliminate the threat from the Super-Soldiers – Dr. X must be stopped at all costs!

end transmission

Virtual Keyboard

ACTION MAN

File Edit View Special Diagnostic Encode

Mission Data: Equipment/Jungle Explorer

Jungle Explorer

Frame: Carbon fibre bonded to aluminium frame with kevlar armour

EFT: Epoxy resin fluid filled all terrain tyres

Top Speed: 175kph

Engine: Mid mounted X15 with twin turbos

Weapons: Two multipurpose Sidewinder missiles. Range 1.5km

Nothing stops this beauty

EDA Secure Channel

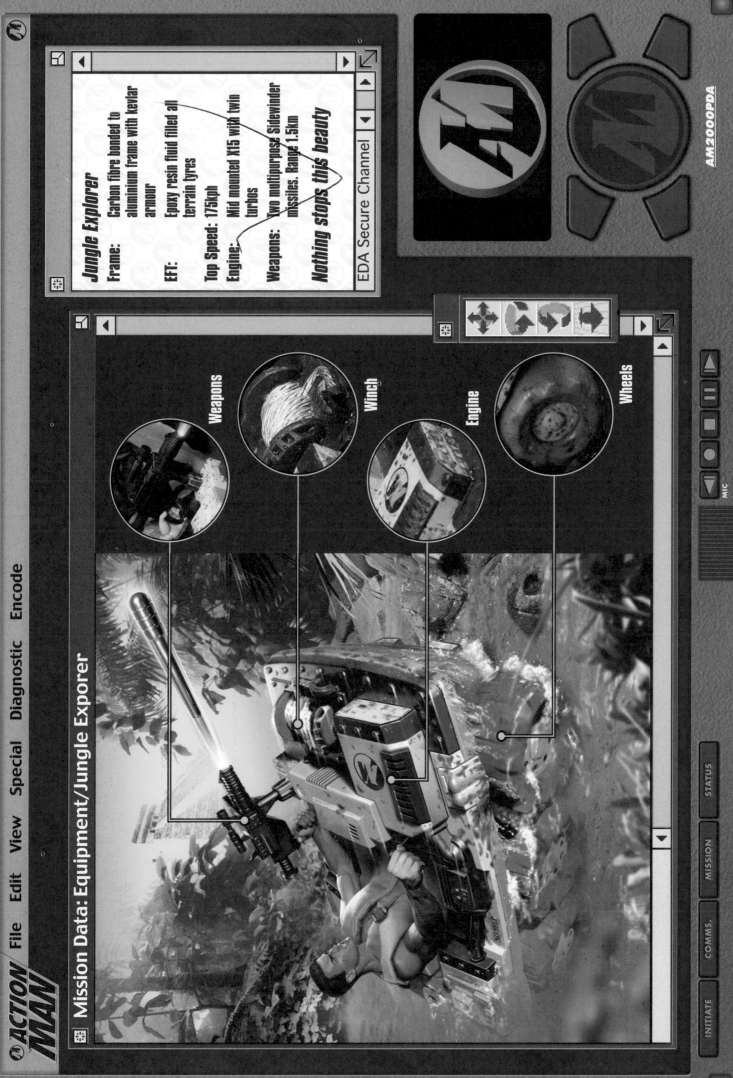

Weapons

Winch

Engine

Wheels

AM2000PDA

MIC

INITIATE COMMS. MISSION STATUS

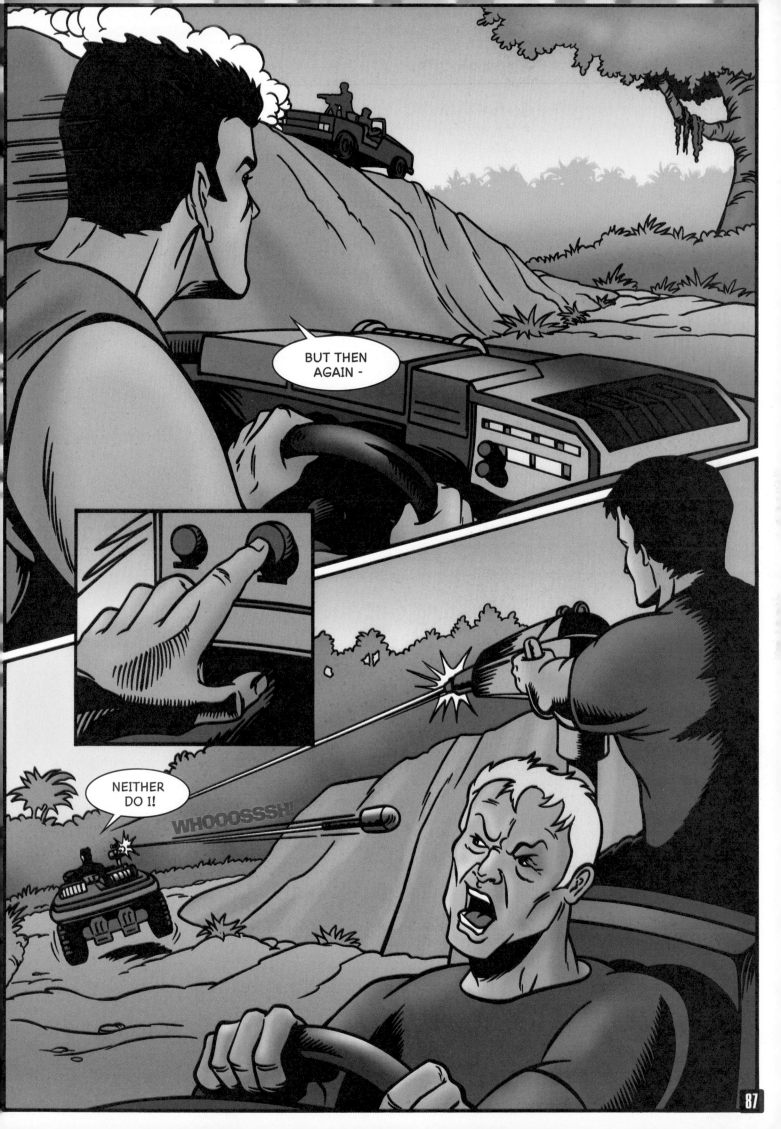

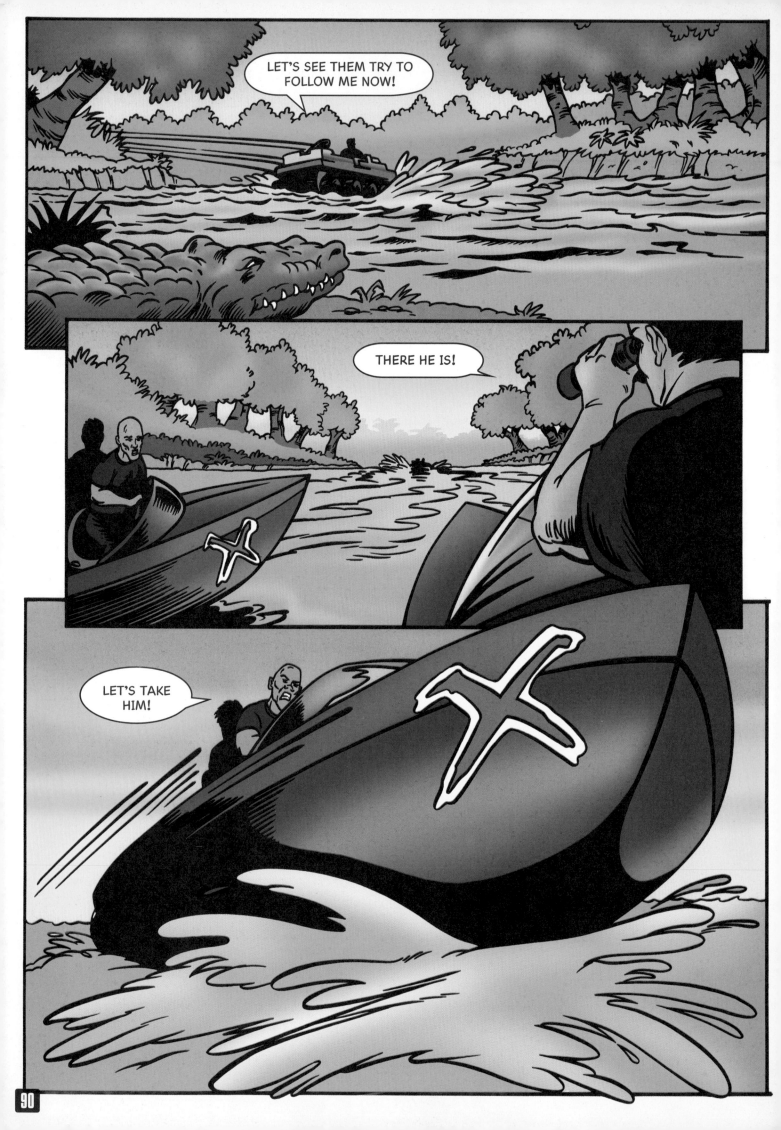

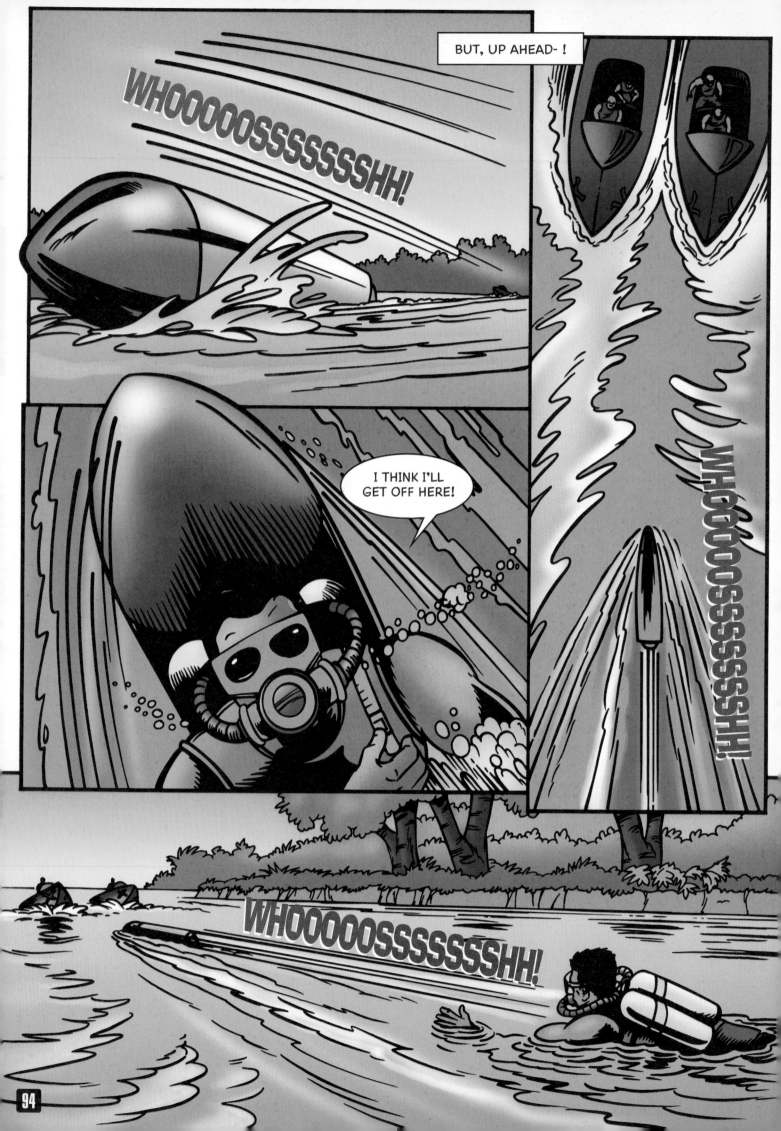

■ Fight to the Death

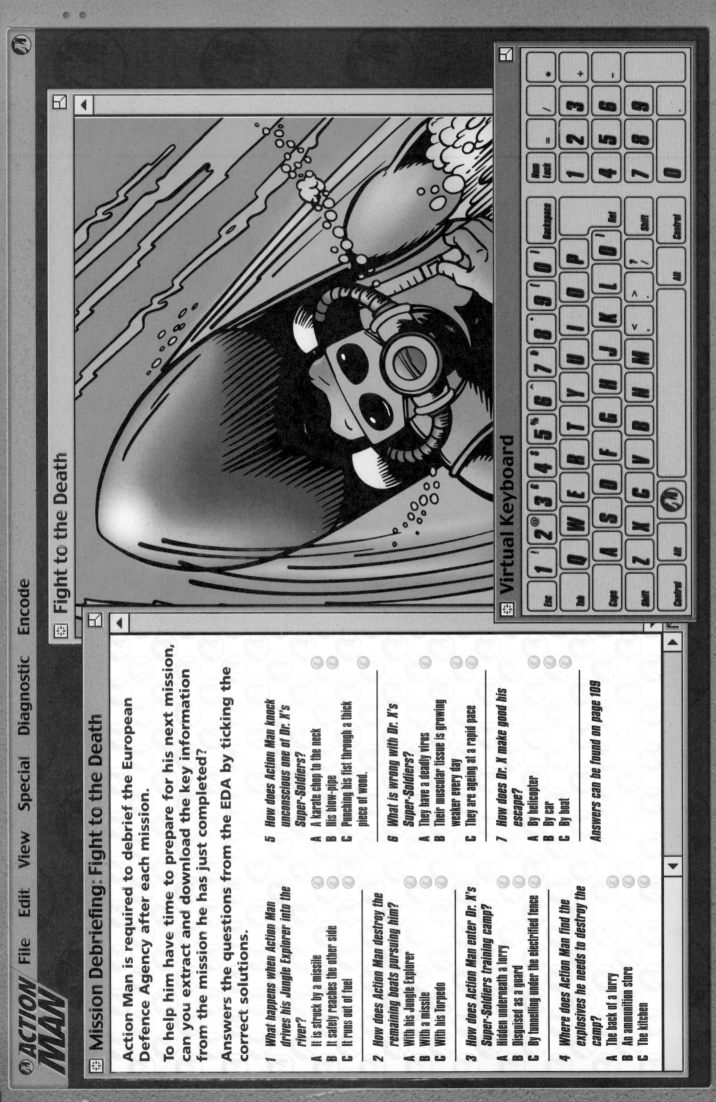

Virtual Keyboard

■ Mission Debriefing: Fight to the Death

Action Man is required to debrief the European Defence Agency after each mission.

To help him have time to prepare for his next mission, can you extract and download the key information from the mission he has just completed?

Answers the questions from the EDA by ticking the correct solutions.

1 What happens when Action Man drives his Jungle Explorer into the river?

A It is struck by a missile
B It safely reaches the other side
C It runs out of fuel

2 How does Action Man destroy the remaining boats pursuing him?

A With his Jungle Explorer
B With a missile
C With his Torpedo

3 How does Action Man enter Dr. X's Super-Soldiers training camp?

A Hidden underneath a lorry
B Disguised as a guard
C By tunneling under the electrified fence

4 Where does Action Man find the explosives he needs to destroy the camp?

A The back of a lorry
B An ammunition store
C The Kitchen

5 How does Action Man knock unconscious one of Dr. X's Super-Soldiers?

A A karate chop to the neck
B His blow-pipe
C Punching his fist through a thick piece of wood.

6 What is wrong with Dr. X's Super-Soldiers?

A They have a deadly virus
B Their muscular tissue is growing weaker every day
C They are ageing at a rapid pace

7 How does Dr. X make good his escape?

A By helicopter
B By car
C By boat

Answers can be found on page 109

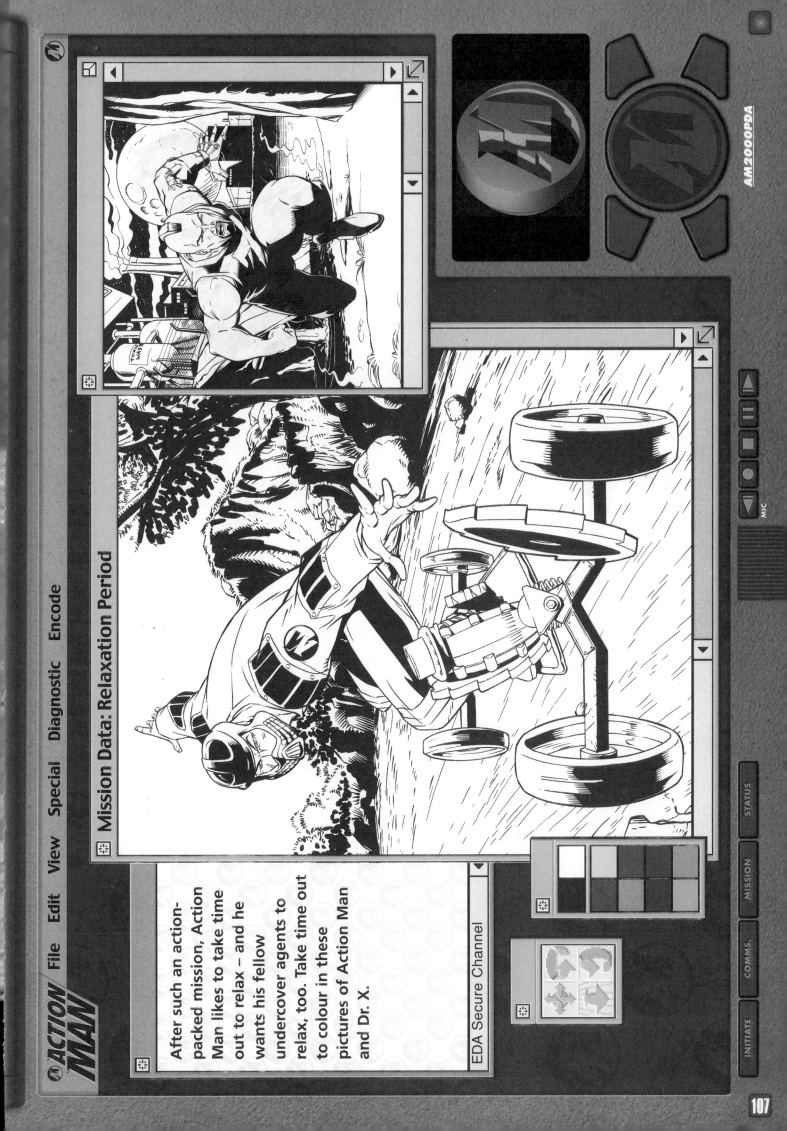

ACTION MAN

File   Edit   View   Special   Diagnostic   Encode

Mission Data: Relaxation Period

After such an action-packed mission, Action Man likes to take time out to relax – and he wants his fellow undercover agents to relax, too. Take time out to colour in these pictures of Action Man and Dr. X.

EDA Secure Channel

AM2000PDA

MIC

STATUS   MISSION   COMMS.   INITIATE

107

ACTION MAN

⊞ Dr. X: Public Enemy Number One

Wanted: Dr. X
– last confirmed sighting the Brazilian Rainforest

Thanks to the determined efforts of Action Man and his fellow EDA Undercover Operatives, Dr. X's latest plan for world domination has been foiled – but Dr. X himself has escaped justice once more.

Dr. X is determined to destroy Action Man and the EDA to stop all interference with his plans. Any sightings of Dr. X must be reported immediately.

Be vigilant! Beware! Dr. X is dangerous, and will strike without warning.

He must be stopped!

Psychological Profile - Dr. X

Name: Dr. X
Age: 30-35
Height: 1.85m
Distinguishing features: Cybernetic eye and hand, X tattoo on chest, mohican haircut.
Psychological Profile: Psychopath, megalomaniac, highly intelligent, ruthless, deadly.

Dr. X is out there, somewhere – be ready for anything

⊞ Dr. X

Survieillance Video

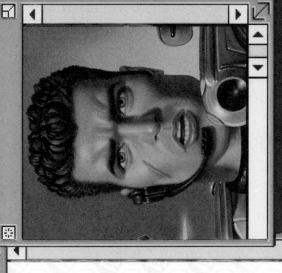

ACTION MAN

File   Edit   View   Special   Diagnostic   Encode

▦ Mission Bioforce: Debriefing

INCOMING E-MAIL – SECURE LINK ENCODING

… Rwtn dyqwzf dr cn asttrj dmlfdsi qbswdf yqvs P ossw qots dr fdre Im. H'f pwfqws etqw dr dqzs rvsm dys jrmti – old pd jqf qtcrfd drr tqds.

Ypf sfuqes csqwf dyqd dys jrmti pf fdptt pw dsmmpots iqwbsm. Ys pf flms dr os etqwpwb qwrdysm qddquz qwn dpcs frrw.

Msermd qwndypwb flfepuprlf dr cs pccsipqdstn – nrl urlti os dys qbswd dyqd apwqttn ystef cs uqedlms Im. H.

Brri tluz!

… DECODING ENCRYPTION

… Only thanks to my fellow trusted agents have I been able to stop Dr. X's insane plan to take over the world – but it was almost too late.

His escape means that the world is still in terrible danger. He is sure to be planning another attack any time soon.

Report anything suspicious to me immediately – you could be the agent that finally helps me capture Dr. X.

Good luck!

[signature]

end transmission.
Mission complete … downloading new data …

Answers from page 106

1 What happens when Action Man drives his Jungle Explorer into the river?
A It is struck by a missile

2 How does Action Man destroy the remaining boats pursuing him?
C With his torpedo

3 How does Action Man enter Dr. X's Super-Soldiers training camp?
B Disguised as a guard

4 Where does Action Man find the explosives he needs to destroy the camp?
B An ammunition store

5 How does Action Man knock unconscious one of Dr. X's Super-Soldiers?
C Punching his fist through a thick piece of wood.

6 What is wrong with Dr. X's Super-Soldiers?
B Their muscular tissue is growing weaker every day

7 How does Dr. X make good his escape?
A By helicopter

EDA Secure Channel

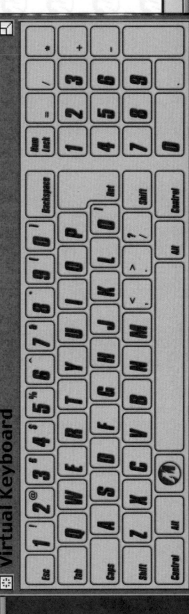

Virtual Keyboard

AM2000PDA

COMMS.   MISSION   STATUS   INITIATE

ACTION MAN

CINEMA

INITIATE   COMMS.   MISSION   STATUS